RUNAWAYS

DEAD END KIDS

WRITER: **JOSS WHEDON**

PENCILER: **MICHAEL RYAN**

INKER: **RICK KETCHAM** WITH **JAY LEISTEN, ANDREW HENNESSY, VICTOR OLAZABA & ROLAND PARIS**

COLORIST: **CHRISTINA STRAIN**

LETTERER: **VC'S RANDY GENTILE, JOE CARAMAGNA & CORY PETIT**

COVER ARTIST: **JO CHEN**

ASSISTANT EDITOR: **DANIEL KETCHUM**

EDITOR: **NICK LOWE**

RUNAWAYS CREATED BY
BRIAN K. VAUGHAN & **ADRIAN ALPHONA**

COLLECTION EDITOR: **JENNIFER GRÜNWALD**

ASSISTANT EDITORS: **CORY LEVINE** & **JOHN DENNING**

EDITOR, SPECIAL PROJECTS: **MARK D. BEAZLEY**

SENIOR EDITOR, SPECIAL PROJECTS: **JEFF YOUNGQUIST**

SENIOR VICE PRESIDENT OF SALES: **DAVID GABRIEL**

PRODUCTION: **JERRY KALINOWSKI**

BOOK DESIGNER: **RODOLFO MURAGUCHI**

EDITOR IN CHIEF: **JOE QUESADA**

PUBLISHER: **DAN BUCKLEY**

DEAD-END KIDS

That's totally her. That's totally She-Hulk.

Victor, we don't have a lot of other options.

I'm not gonna talk to this guy. I'm just here if things get ugly.

Things *are* ugly. They're all ugly.

Is somebody gonna deal with She-Hulk having scampi like three tables away?

I just don't want you pawing me when you look like that.

My love, we have to show *strength* here. My male form is more intimidating.

That's sexist.

And the man we're meeting isn't?

She-Hulk has the fakest boobs I ever saw.

And those aren't scampies, they're shrimp.

Vic, you gotta check this out. I'm not into muscles but, I'm, now I'm sort of into muscles.

Is she gonna be a problem, being here? Wasn't she an Avenger?

What's she gonna do? We're just having dinner.

Yeah, but isn't this guy we're meeting supposed to be the most evil person in the whole...

...stuff?

Children.

Kingpin.

"Mr. Fisk" will be fine.

Mr. Fisk. You know who we are?

I'm having dinner with you, at my expense, at my restaurant.

Skip the remedial questions or have someone else speak for the group.

'86 Chateau Lafitte and another round for the children.

You can stop calling us that any time, Shamu.

We represent the Pride.

I *respect* the Pride.

They ran Los Angeles with efficiency and vision. They never tried to muscle into my city, nor I into theirs.

Are you saying you represent their interests now?

They're dead. We represent *our* interests.

We haven't decided.

We want to spend some time in New York, and we'd like to do it without the Avengers or anybody else tracking us down. We know you dealt with our parents...

Do you expect them to conflict or coincide with my own?

You want a favor.

A show of faith.

No, it's a favor.

Why don't we call it an investment?

I dislike semantics.

Yeah, so does Mel Gibson. Where's that *"respect"* you were supposed to be all up in?

This isn't a frikkin' classroom, fat-ass.

Don't be a meanie! He's probably got glands!

This *isn't* a classroom, Mr. Stein.

Several months ago Mr. Stein and Ms. Minoru encountered a street-level thug who called himself *"Pusher-Man"*.

You duped him into thinking he had an *"in"* with the new incarnation of the Pride.

Excited, he brought this information to an associate, who brought it to me.

His error was clear to me.

What I'd like you to note is the *manner* of his death, the time taken, the pieces removed, before he succumbed.

This man had powers as well.

Now whether you purport to be the new Pride, or are touting your prowess at having ended them, you all know this:

I will go where you will not. That is why you'll lose.

You're not the Pride. You're a group of kids on the run who want a place to hide.

I'm going to do you that favor.

And you will do one for me.

A second chance.

You are ever my angel.

You have to be freezing.

Kar! Thanks. I forgot what it's like here.

You're not cold?

No, I'm good.

I suck so hard.

This isn't your fault.

Victor's right: I totally folded in that meeting.

The Kingpin *targeted* you. You go after the strong ones first--that's, like, the first rule. He shook us *all* up.

I think Xavin has a crush on him.

Uchh. She's such a *guy* sometimes...

Is she?

I mean... does she really change, or...I mean, as a Skrull was he-- she born with... ...please make me stop.

It's hard for people to get.

You guys just seem to see things really differently.

We do, but when she's alone with me...

But is that real? The real her?

What are you doing?

No! I'm sorry--

Xavin found out I was gay and didn't so much as blink. She's not *pretending* to be a woman; she's learning to be a *human*.

She's trying to change. Become better. You see anyone else making that effort?

I just--

She doesn't fit in, great. Isn't that what this group is supposed to be all about?

I'm not trying to get between you guys. Xavin's cool--

She's more than that.

She gives me something you can't.

"I promise to be gentle."

THOOM!

Gnntl?

It was a precision landing.

"Gentle" means "We didn't break the roof".

I told you like ten times to stay out of my stuff.

But we're heisting! Why couldn't you wear normal-person stockings anyway? I'm gonna have waffle-face.

Just a couple m[ore] second[s], honey.

Buncha old junk. You sure about this place?

I think so. Yes.

I mean, isn't rent in New York insane? No way this is just somebody's attic.

Yeah, I'm feeling a massive security matrix. Lasers, alarms...lotta backup systems. I can't manipulate this.

All I can do is blow it out. It'll probably alert the police.

Or possibly S.H.I.E.L.D....

We'll be long gone.

Blow it.

This way.

You're sure?

Everybody stop asking me that.

Children.

AAGH!

We have to find Chase!

He's using children.

I shouldn't be surprised. Children are always in the front lines of a war.

At least this won't take long.

One look at me and they're frozen. Like they're looking at the angel of death.

WHUMP

Punisher's war
journal:
Hhhhhhhh....

The Kingpin hadda know we'd figure this out. He's playing with us.

And he expects us to hand it over to him.

...e don't, he'll robably kill us pretty horribly.

I have a plan. Let Molly hit him.

I'm not hitting anybody else that doesn't have powers.

Especially when they've got glands.

One more complication. Can I just have a do-over for the last two days?

We could have avoided all of this if I thought ahead a little.

Regret is a luxury.

Then meet the richest people on earth.

We're here, it's now, we gotta deal. Just think it through...

"...and hope we catch a break."

MARVEL · M · NEW YORK. NY.
EXTRA FINISH.

We're a hundred years from home.

THE NEW YORK HERALD.

WHOLE NO. 24601   NEW YORK, WEDNESDAY, JUNE 27, 1907   PRICE, FOUR CE...

TYPHOID MARY APPREHENDED
Typhus Terror At An End.

Wow. This is *amazingly* bad.

Should you be sitting? That healing spell--

--worked great. I'm fine, except for the amazingly bad.

"Typhoid Mary." Didn't she fight Daredevil?

We have to get back to our time as soon as possible.

Our time where men are attacking us with missiles and ninjas?

Yeah, we were like three seconds from being blown to bits, which I've sort of had enough of.

As usual, you're missing the bigger issue. What you should be worried about is the Butterfly Effect.

Dude, I'm totally on top of the Butterfly Effect!

What were they, like, bigger?

I don't think it'll be a problem--which is the good news, since we're going nowhere.

But if we mess with the time stream, don't we end up never being born, or Hitler won, or something?

Well, if the... what is it, Yorkes? Gert's parents--if they were time travelers they'd have to have some kind of fail-safe, some protective bubble or something to keep them from effecting major change, or they'd never come back to the same future twice.

They'd also have to have a power source good for a round trip. We can't assume anything is working in our favor.

We also can't hide in an alley and do nothing.

You're not even pretending to contain your excitement.

How often do we get this chance? A world we've never seen!

You've seen many worlds--

But this is our planet. Our history. We're living in history.

Right. We're living in something I flunked. How do we make it go away?

Inky.

I vote spell.

Moll with
e call! Staff
up, Minoru.

That's a
big order...

Yeah, if
it goes
wrong--

There's
s in knickers
t there.
riously. I'll
cut you.

NEGATIVE.

HOLO-RECORDS
INDICATE I AM
IMPERVIOUS TO
SPELL-CASTING.

Wait
a sec.
"Holo"?

Can
you--

ACCESSING.

There's
the little
#&$%er.

This'll
spot-weld
the housing
in.

I'm not
familiar--

Ah, it's
quasi-sentient.
Just hold it
close.

A frog?
I wouldn't
have expected
such a
whimsical
design,
Victor.

Blame Janet. But it'll
go where a plane
won't--it's good
in a jam.

So are
these. Dale and I still
can't muster up the big
time jumps, but these
are perfect for
quick escapes.

How far
back can
they go?

Hello?

Is somebody here with me?

Turn it off.

All right, we heard them. There might be another one of those things somewhere.

It would be in Los Angeles, surely?

There wasn't any Los Angeles worth mentioning back then. Now.

The one we found was in New York--it could be sitting there right now!

Building wasn't that old. But the Yorkes traveled a lot, not just in time.

Trying to find another device is our best shot.

Yay. I mean, I'm all about the mission, but yay.

Killer spell, Nico. I'm sweating so much I *know* we blend right in.

I just wish I'd had time to sew them. I am getting so many ideas from this era...I mean, look at those boots!

...because of the mission.

You sure Old Lace'll be cool in that alley?

Nope. But somebody's gotta watch the frog. Even while it's invisible?

I didn't say *"watch over the frog".* I said watch it.

This cannot stand! Sweatshop owners are Tsars of New World! This very building--

I don't think Leapfrog meant to freak you out. *I* certainly never --

It's not you, man. Frog's calling its own shots.

I mean, why didn't it show us that stuff *before* we time-boogied?

UNFAIR
UNSAFE
UNETHICAL

SWEATSHOPS ARE SLAVESH...

...OMEN
...ILDREN
...ASJ?

How much of that thing is just my dad?

They're all children...

Anybody else? Can anybody hear me?

Huh?

Hey! Are you okay?

"We can't stick around and get noticed."

At least nobody had a camera. Unless...do they have cameras now?

Yeah, but not on their phones or anything.

If I might ask...

...where do you expect to be going?

Tristan. Pleasure to meet you all.

We got a room for you, all your own. Some grub and a night's rest is what you need.

We have to talk.

Alone, Nico.

Lillie? You gonna leave me alone up there or can you manage another whirl?

This is the girls' side! No boys are allowed on this side of the room for smooching or any other gross stuff that I can usually hear even when we're not in the same room.

I just worry about you.

I'll be fine.

We have to get out of this time as soon as we can.

Which is why I don't wanna miss this chance. I'm just gonna look around.

Have fun. And then stop having fun and come back.

I'd kiss you if you were a chick.

No smooching means you two, too!

That's all? He gave you that message and let you go?

He said I'd know who and when to give it. I don't see how...

I don't even know what it *means*. But running into him again can't be a coincidence.

And what the hell happened...happened to his face? Do we cause that? No, 'cause then we would have...

Madre de Dios, this time-travel logic makes my circuits short.

Yeah, I smelled something burning when you met Miss Dance-On-Air, too.

What, Lillie? Please, she's clearly into Tristan.

That... wasn't the right response, was it?

Wow.

Ties! Ties and stiff white collars!

And wow.

Also, wow.

May I escort you somewhere?

Oh, I'm fine, thank you.

Excuse me, miss?

Come on. I've got rooms, and plenty a' dust--more than you'll make out here.

Hey!

Don't be coy; it doesn't suit.

A girl out alone at night's looking for one thing only.

And that's what I got right here.

The only reason anyone trusts you is that stick.

So yes, I trust you. But it bothers me that I do.

I seen these kids in action and I'm telling you, they're the genuine article.

I coulda gone to the Upward Path, they're sniffin' for recruits but I sez "No, get to the Mineola, talk to Maneater; he'll treat you square."

And what's your idea of square?

Finder's fee, plus a remembrance for any job they pull...

...maybe a word in for me with...you know... the Others?

You don't say their names. They never hear yours. This ensures your continued existence. You're close to crossing a line here that you must not cross.

They don't call me Maneater for any reason other than the obvious.

If there's really a war coming, these kids are gonna tip the scale.

I come to you in good faith, I get threatened with ingestion.

In good faith I came.

Hunh.

Come in.

Forgive me for interrupting.

Not at all.

We have word of a new gang of Wonders, possibly powerful.

They're holed up with the Street Arabs. Things being as they are, I thought we could use a little muscle.

Well we certainly can't have them falling to the other side.

Absolutely. Recruit them...

The usual procedure?

Eat up, friends. Sweet rolls and fresh ham-hocks!

All these new words!

Nothing vegan, I'm guessing...

Knock yourself out.

You *stud!*

We got marching orders, Nico? 'Cause I've been talking with The Swell here...

As I learn you're after a priceless object no bigger than that apple, and in a burg of this magnitude, I figure you got just a few options.

You go to the Merchant's Trust and ask them to open the vaults, which they most certainly will not...

...or you go to the Mineola.

The Mineola?

Private subway train, owned by the very powerful people who run the Sinners.

And who are these very powerful people?

Well they prefer to keep their identities secret.

You cn tll us...

Secret, ah...from me.

But us Arabs job for 'em now and again, and if there's anyone in New York knows where the goodies is kept, it's them.

And their group is called the Sinners because they're solid citizens, right?

Back to business.

I think we should split up. It's our best chance of finding a new...the overdrive device.

What happened to the old one?

The overdrive...I tossed it in an alley.

Well that's muffin-headed, you don't mind my saying.

Lillie...

If it's a machine at all Professor Duck can make it work--he built Tristan his wings!

Please tell me the guy's a duck.

Nah, he's a Chinee, same as dear Miss Nico here.

Bit cracked, as well. Your best bet's the Sinners, my word on that.

First of all, I'm from Japan. By way of Glendale.

Second, we're still splitting up.

Chase, you and Xavin can check out the Mineola, meet these Sinners. Maybe we can make some kind of deal with them if they've got the goods.

A deal? Didn't we just *leave* that party? With rockets on our ass?

You wanna party like it's 1899, be my guest. I'm going back.

Lillie. Spieler. Whatever you...would you bring someone to see this professor if we got the device?

Glad to help.

Great. Take Victor.

Nico? Can I slip out for a few hours?

More sight-seeing?

No, it's... I need to do something, and...

...I thought Molly could come with.

Yes! *Not* picked last!

What about you?

I'm gonna go to the Merchant's Trust.

And ask them to open the vaults.

And if you don't find work, don't bother coming home!

I promise--

Promise does not warm my belly! Your mother may have spoiled you rotten, little Klara, but she's gone now.

Bring home some money or you'll be gone as well!

Excuse me...

Klara? I'm Karolina Dean, this is Molly Hayes.

We wanted to talk to you about yesterday. At the factory...

I don't want any Union, thank you, the Unions are not good...

If I'm seen talking to you...

It's not about a Union.

It's about your power.

You're a Wonder.

I saw the vines you climbed down. The roses. You made them grow, didn't you?

I know nothing. I have to go.

But we're Wonders too!

Wow.

You lads put those scum to rights.

I'll bring down the Spieler.

Oh, look.

Metal.

Open Sesame.

Now how do we dispose of the girl?

I think she needs a serious time-out.

This stuff is getting to her, Xav. Maybe it's the magic...

Working for the Kingpin may have been shortsighted, but that doesn't mean these "Sinners" are necessarily--

Dude, I'm talking about *Vic!*

He and that Spieler chick are vibing like crazy and Nico practically shoves him into her arms!

I'm the one who notices this? Aren't you a *girl* part of the time?

Yes, but sometimes I wonder if I'm the *right* girl.

I thought Karolina wanted to be with Nico, and I... I tried pretending I was--

Niiice...

Well, there's no point in holding on to someone who--

Dude, I'm talking about the *train!*

Whatdaya got?

Excuse me?

Powers. Specialties. What can you bring me I don't already have?

Ahh, these two is amazing! Show Mr. Maneater how you're amazing.

I don't do tricks unless I get a treat.

You do what I say.

You're not the boss of me, big guy, and you know what? I don't think you're the boss of *you*, either.

The private train is really cool but I can smell the engine in here. I bet it's noisy, too.

The sweet ride's back there, right? So why don't you talk to the people in the papoose and tell them they got *real* business.

It's a good thing I skipped lunch.

CRA-CHH!!

Is Gertrude with you?

Gertrude would never waste her time with this ape.

Oh no.

Gert and me never wasted a *second*.

Hey, tell me which is worse? That Gert was in love with me...

..or that she's *dead.*

You son of a AUNNH!

We have to go, Chase!

Mhhff... frrgve me...

Oh, we shoulda brought you here sooner! We just forgot you'd be hungry when you made us both wanna barf.

Brrf?

Well, like we said, where we're from, things are really different.

It's against the law to make someone your age work, let alone get married. You'd be in school right now.

Yeah, every kid gets to go to school!

'cept us...

...and Dakota Fanning...

When did you find out about your powers? If you don't mind talking about it...

I have always just...I thought that was how plants grew.

Because you asked them to.

On our farm in Bern, I would speak and the crops would listen. But the roses...

The roses would speak back.

My mother thought it was unnatural. She was relieved to find me a husband that was sailing far away. She said I shamed God, and never to speak of my cur...my power.

Mr. Prast is a devout man, but he...drinks. He does not find work.

While you slave away at a factory? Lame-o!

It is not so bad. It is just, when I come home so tired, and then he...I do not enjoy it. My...

...my marital duties.

Oh, my God...

He makes you do *chores*?!?

He just *left?*

He took the Yorkes' time-travel device and was gone.

Did he say--

Nothing. Just looked at me with...I think it was regret. Or... Apology.

I don't think he's coming back.

Pfft! He's so coming back. Prb'ly with cool weapons or a thing.

Time machine...?

What about Vic and Nico?

You haven't checked in with them?

I'm telling you, this bunch has put us on Queer Street with the Sinners.

We've had black marks in their book before...

Not like this.

Maneater'll probably kill me for even seein' 'em.

George. We just gotta keep 'em close till I can find Maneater in a less... maneating mood.

If it's a question of brains, perhaps being eaten...

I say toss 'em out 'fore it gets worse.

I say what Hoyden said, mainly because she said it.

Now now, let's not be impulsive. This could still work to our advantage.

As, perhaps, a deal.

...should be concentrating on getting home, not picking up strays!

Xavin, if you had any concept what this girl's been through...

They're arguing about me.

I know! It's SO awkward!

Ahhhh... Verrry boring...

Uh, that's a time-traveling device.

No, this is *shell* of time-traveling device. Power source is used up.

Power source is from future. So not invented yet. So boring.

Well, do you have, um, any *other* way for us to get to the future?

Yes!

Live very long time! Future come without machine!

TA-HA-HA-HA-HA...

eh heh...we all ime machines! Oh, so funny for me...

I'm sorry, Victor... It's not your fault.

But what if you don't find a way? What if you can't get back to your own time?

Would you maybe stay here?

Lillie, I... You're amazing; I never...but it's... ...well, it's not simple.

It is for me.

Really? 'Cause from where I'm standing... (...I mean *exactly* where I'm standing...)

Wait...Tristan? You think we--

You guys seem pretty tight...

"Tight"? What's that? You implying I'm some sort of notch-house dove?

Uh, no?

Tristan's like m'brother and that's it.

He know that?

Victor, if you're stayin' I'm yours for good and all. That's just how it is.

And if I'm not staying?

Lillie, I'm not planning to stay. My friends and I have to get back to where we belong, and when we do...

War don't rage in my city without me getting a piece.

Give them one.

And war is what we'll make. The Upward Path has been praying for a reason to sweep those streets clean.

Depend on it.

He's a good soldier.

It's a pity he'll be caught in it too.

The poorer neighborhoods always burn, Dale, and the riff-raff go up with them.

Let them start their war. You concentrate on finishing it.

One of the Yorkes.

If they've taken Leapfrog we'll be trapped here!

No... We still have time. But we have to move now.

What about the big war?

Don't worry. It'll still be here when we get back.

Hunnnnh...

Made it... thank you, Lord...

Thank you for protecting me.

I don't understand. A message from the future?

I didn't understand either. But it makes sense now.

Tell me again.

"This is your last dance. Your chance to change your fate. Leave this world for a better one..."

"...or waste your days in regret."

I pulled a few bits out of the overdrive device. Figured they'd show up and try to use it once I took their time-ride.

I miss much?

Only a *war*, dorkface.

What do we do about the Yorkes? Nico, you can't use *"Forget"* again, can you?

Why would I want to do that?

The show must go on.

They'll go back to when they came from. And they'll know. What happens to Gert, what happens to them, they'll know every second it's coming.

They won't be able to change anything they do. Or say anything. Not even to each other. For all the world their short, useless lives will play out exactly like they did before. But inside...

...they'll never stop screaming.

Mol... Molly...?

Please...

Klara!

What happened? Who did this?

I'm sorry...

I know who did this.

And I know where he lives.

We don't have time, Kar.

We're all here. This is the time to bail.

What about her?

We bring her with us!

You'll come, right?

You'd... still have me?

Well, you have to no be stupid about gay or freak out 'cause there's jetplanes but *yeah!*

Couple new faces. I can rock that.

Gonna be tight in the frog...

But I was.

I never loved anyone so much, not ever again, and I could be starting my life with him right now.

I sent him to me and still I didn't...how could I be such a child?

A stupid, scared child...

I could have thrived in the present. It would have been wonderful...

I could have skipped all those years wishing... waiting...

...watching the city change in every way that doesn't matter...

...and waiting to send him back. For nothing.

Maybe he failed.

To give you the message.

He gave me the message, Tristan.

He always does.

Mein Gott...

Don't worry. L.A. is way better than New York. Everybody thinks so.

You think the Kingpin'll come after us?

All we did was keep what was ours.

"Pin's a businessman. Once we're off his turf he'll just go back to business."

"What about the Punisher?"

"Wow, I totally forgot about him."

Still... standing...

I can't believe I used to think that guy was cool.

So I guess we're pretty much okay.

Didn't say that.

Sucks that c's new girl issed out at the last second.

You didn't have anything to do with that, did you? Kinda looks like you've got the juice...

You kidding? I practically threw her at him.

Yeah, I didn't exactly follow that either.

Are you really that remedial?

They were in love.

Like, stupid, first-sight, courtly head-over-heels Romeo and Juliet love. Everybody knew it.

What was I gonna do, fight?

I don't know why Lillie chickened out. If I'd felt like that...

But I never have.

I have this, oh, pathological need to insert myself between people...

...which you well remember...

...and I thought I'd try the other thing for once.

That people have spent more than a hundred years fighting over a city that doesn't even have *In-n-Out Burger*.

Yeah, let's go home.

Haven't heard *that* word in a while...

So we don't know where we're going.

"Still beats living in the past."

THE END.

NICO & KAROLINA

Darkgrey-Black

White

See-through Black

Edwardian Style.

White

grey

Black

Sleeves/Trim lighter than Skirt and Bodice

Hairstyle only lasts till she lets glow.

Collar Whiter Cream

She'll roll up the Sleeves when she says she's Hot

Brass Buttons

Two Part Skirt.

Not sure How much color we get in 1907

White or Creme

Brown?

CHASE

NICO

CHARACTER SKETCHES
BY MICHAEL RYAN

MOLLY

KAROLINA

XAVIN

VICTOR